G000093858

Then God said,
"Let the land produce vegetation:
seed-bearing plants and trees on the
land that bear fruit with seed in it."
Genesis 1:11

God created an amazing world full of delicious things to
eat!

"The Lord God took the man and put him in the Garden of Eden to work it and take care of it."
Genesis 2:15

God made people and put them in charge of the land so they could look after the world and grow their own food.

"As long as the earth endures,
seedtime and harvest,
cold and heat,
summer and winter,
day and night
will never cease."
Genesis 8:22

After the big flood, God promised Noah there would always be seasons. Everyone would know when it was the right time to plant seeds and when to harvest them.

"The land will yield its harvest,
and God, our God, will bless us."
Psalm 67:6

At Harvest time farmers gather their crops because they are ripe. These crops are made into the food we buy in the shops, like our fruit and vegetables, bread and cereals.

"Give us each day our daily bread."
Luke 11:3

When Jesus taught us how to pray, he said we could ask God to provide us with the food we need each day.

"Celebrate the Feast of Harvest with the firstfruits of the crops you sow in your field."
Exodus 23:16

At Harvest time it's a really good idea to say a special "thank you" to God for all we have to eat.

Look at the birds of the air; they do not sow or reap or store away in barns, and yet your heavenly Father feeds them. Are you not much more valuable than they?
Matt 6:26

Jesus says we can learn a good lesson from the birds. They don't spend all day worrying about what's for tea! They trust God to provide their food and don't forget, we are even more special to God than the birds!

"When you reap the harvest of your land, do not reap to the very edges of your field or gather the gleanings of your harvest. Do not go over your vineyard a second time or pick up the grapes that have fallen. Leave them for the poor."
Leviticus 19:9-10

The Bible says it is good to share what we have with others who are in need. Sometimes we take more than we need when we could share what we have with others.

"Remember this: Whoever sows sparingly will also reap sparingly, and whoever sows generously will also reap generously. Each man should give what he has decided in his heart to give, not reluctantly or under compulsion, for God loves a cheerful giver. And God is able to make all grace abound to you, so that in all things at all times, having all that you need, you will abound in every good work."
2 Corinthians 9:6-8

Paul said in one of his letters to a Church in Corinth, the more we give, the better we feel. God will bless us if we are happy to share!!

God said to him, "You fool! This very night your life will be demanded from you. Then who will get what you have prepared for yourself?" This is how it will be with anyone who stores up things for himself but is not rich towards God"
Luke 12:20-21

In "The Parable of the Rich Fool" Jesus warns us not to be like the man in the story. The rich fool kept everything he grew on his land for himself and did not share it with others.

"A farmer went out to sow his seed. As he was scattering the seed, some fell along the path; it was trampled on, and the birds of the air ate it up. Some fell on rock, and when it came up, the plants withered because they had no moisture. Other seed fell among thorns, which grew up with it and choked the plants. Still other seed fell on good soil. It came up and yielded a crop, a hundred times more than was sown."
Luke 8: 5-8

Jesus told a great story called "The Parable of The Sower." The farmer sowing the seed is like someone spreading the good news about Jesus. The story helps us to think about what we do when we've heard the good news.

"But the seed on good soil stands for those with a noble and good heart, who hear the word, retain it, and by persevering produce a crop."
Luke 8:15

When we listen to God and do things his way, God helps us to grow strong in our faith and do amazing things for him. We become just like a plant in good soil, growing strong and producing delicious fruit.

"The harvest is plentiful but the workers are few."
Matt 9:37

Jesus says people who want to find out about him are like fields of crops waiting to be harvested. We can help Jesus by telling others about him.

"Let us not become weary in doing good, for at the proper time we will reap a harvest if we do not give up"
Galatians 6:9

Never give up trying to be helpful and doing good things. It might be hard work but it will be worth it in the end!

The Rainbow Colouring Book Range...

Colours in the Bible

Food in the Bible

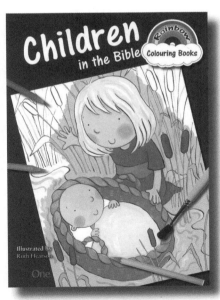

Children in the Bible

The Armour of God

Available from Day One

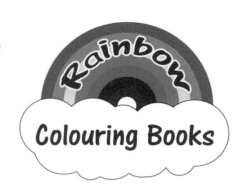

Colouring Books

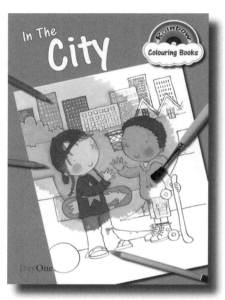

In the City

On the Beach

In the Country

On the Farm

© **Day One Publications 2013**

ISBN 978-1-84625-396-6

Scripture quotations are from The New International Version

Published by Day One Publications
Ryelands Road, Leominster, HR6 8NZ
Email: Sales@dayone.co.uk | www.dayone.co.uk
Tel: +44 (0) 1568 613 740 | Fax: 01568 611 473
Tel: Toll Free 888 329 6630 (North America)

All rights reserved

No part of this publication may be reproduced, or stored in a retrieval system, or transmitted, in any form or by any means, mechanical, electronic, photocopying, recording or otherwise, without the prior permission of Day One Publications.

Illustrations: Ruth Hearson   **Design:** Elk-Design.co.uk   **Printed by** Active Colour - Redruth